POPULAR LECTURES IN MATHEMATICS SERIES

EDITORS: I. N. SNEDDON AND M. STARK

Volume 6

INEQUALITIES

TITLES IN THE POPULAR LECTURES IN MATHEMATICS SERIES

INEQUALITIES

by
P. P. KOROVKIN

Translated from the Russian by
HALINA MOSS, B.Sc.

Translation Editor
IAN N. SNEDDON
Simson Professor of Mathematics
in the University of Glasgow

BLAISDELL PUBLISHING COMPANY
NEW YORK · LONDON
A DIVISION OF RANDOM HOUSE

SOLE DISTRIBUTORS IN THE UNITED STATES AND CANADA
Blaisdell Publishing Company
22 East 51st Street, New York 22, N.Y.

A translation of the original volume
Neravenstva
(Moscow-Leningrad, Gostekhizdat, 1952)

Library of Congress Card Number: 61-11526

Printed in Great Britain by Pergamon Printing and Art Services Limited, London

CONTENTS

FOREWORD

In a high school course of mathematics pupils become acquainted with the properties of inequalities and with methods of solving them in the simplest cases - inequalities of first and second degree.

The author does not aim at setting forth the basic properties of inequalities. He merely tries to acquaint pupils of higher classes of schools with some remarkable inequalities which have played a large part in various branches of higher mathematics, and with their application as far as finding the greatest and the least values of numbers, and the calculation of some limits.

This book has 62 problems, of which 36, with their detailed solutions, comprise the bulk of the book, and the remaining 26 problems are given as exercises at the end of Sections 1, 4 and 5. The reader will find their solutions at the end of the book.

The independent solution of a few difficult problems will undoubtedly be more useful to the pupil than the solving of many simple ones.

We suggest therefore that the pupil turns to the solutions only after he has found an independent solution, possibly differing (which is very good!) from the solution indicated by the author. In proving the inequalities and solving the problems, the author uses only familiar elementary properties of inequalities and limits.

1. ELEMENTARY INEQUALITIES

The integral part of the number x (denoted $[x]$) is the greatest whole number not exceeding x.

It follows from this definition that $[x] \leqslant x$, as the integral part does not exceed x. On the other hand, since $[x]$ is the greatest whole number satisfying the latter inequality $[x] + 1 > x$.

Thus, $[x]$ is a whole number defined by the inequalities

$$[x] \leqslant x < [x] + 1.$$

In this way, for example, from the inequalities

$$3 < \pi < 4, \quad 5 < \frac{17}{3} < 6, \quad -2 < -\sqrt{2} < -1, \quad 5 = 5 < 6$$

it follows that

$$[\pi] = 3, \quad \left[\frac{17}{3}\right] = 5, \quad [-\sqrt{2}] = -2, \quad [5] = 5.$$

<u>Problem 1.</u> Find the integral part of the number

$$x = 1 + \frac{1}{\sqrt{2}} + \frac{1}{\sqrt{3}} + \frac{1}{\sqrt{4}} + \frac{1}{\sqrt{5}}.$$

S o l u t i o n. We shall make use of the inequalities

$$1 \leqslant \quad 1 \quad \leqslant 1.$$
$$0.7 < \sqrt{\frac{1}{2}} < 0.8,$$
$$0.5 < \sqrt{\frac{1}{3}} < 0.6,$$
$$0.5 \leqslant \sqrt{\frac{1}{4}} \leqslant 0.5,$$
$$0.4 < \sqrt{\frac{1}{5}} < 0.5$$

1

(They are obtained when the square root is extracted to the nearest 0.1 above or below). Adding these inequalities we obtain

$$1+0.7+0.5+0.5+0.4 < x < 1+0.8+0.6+0.5+0.5,$$

i.e. $3.1 < x < 3.4$ and therefore $[x] = 3$.

Problem 2. Find the integral part of the number

$$y = 1 + \frac{1}{\sqrt{2}} + \frac{1}{\sqrt{3}} + \frac{1}{\sqrt{4}} + \cdots + \frac{1}{\sqrt{1,000,000}}.$$

S o l u t i o n. This problem differs from the preceding one only in the number of terms to be added; in the first case 5, in the second case 1,000,000. This very circumstance renders the previous method of solution inapplicable in practice.

To solve this problem we study the sum

$$1 + \frac{1}{\sqrt{2}} + \frac{1}{\sqrt{3}} + \frac{1}{\sqrt{4}} + \cdots + \frac{1}{\sqrt{n}}.$$

For this we shall prove the inequalities

$$2\sqrt{n+1} - 2\sqrt{n} < \frac{1}{\sqrt{n}} < 2\sqrt{n} - 2\sqrt{n-1}. \qquad (1)$$

Indeed, since

$$2\sqrt{n+1} - 2\sqrt{n} = \frac{2(\sqrt{n+1} - \sqrt{n})(\sqrt{n+1} + \sqrt{n})}{\sqrt{n+1} + \sqrt{n}} =$$
$$= \frac{2}{\sqrt{n+1} + \sqrt{n}},$$

and

$$\sqrt{n+1} > \sqrt{n},$$

then

$$2\sqrt{n+1} - 2\sqrt{n} < \frac{2}{2\sqrt{n}} = \frac{1}{\sqrt{n}}.$$

Thus, the first part of the inequality (1) has been proved. The second part is proved similarly.

Letting (1) $n = 2, 3, 4, \ldots, n$, in the inequalities (1) we get

$$2\sqrt{3} - 2\sqrt{2} < \frac{1}{\sqrt{2}} < 2\sqrt{2} - 2,$$

$$2\sqrt{4} - 2\sqrt{3} < \frac{1}{\sqrt{3}} < 2\sqrt{3} - 2\sqrt{2},$$

$$2\sqrt{5} - 2\sqrt{4} < \frac{1}{\sqrt{4}} < 2\sqrt{4} - 2\sqrt{3},$$

$$\cdots\cdots\cdots\cdots\cdots\cdots\cdots\cdots\cdots$$

$$2\sqrt{n+1} - 2\sqrt{n} < \frac{1}{\sqrt{n}} < 2\sqrt{n} - 2\sqrt{n-1}.$$

Now, adding these inequalities we have

$$2\sqrt{n+1} - 2\sqrt{2} <$$

$$< \frac{1}{\sqrt{2}} + \frac{1}{\sqrt{3}} + \frac{1}{\sqrt{4}} + \ldots + \frac{1}{\sqrt{n}} < 2\sqrt{n} - 2.$$

Adding 1 to each part of the inequalities obtained, we find that

$$2\sqrt{n+1} - 2\sqrt{2} + 1 <$$

$$< 1 + \frac{1}{\sqrt{2}} + \frac{1}{\sqrt{3}} + \frac{1}{\sqrt{4}} + \ldots + \frac{1}{\sqrt{n}} < 2\sqrt{n} - 1. \qquad (2)$$

As $2\sqrt{2} < 3$, and $\sqrt{n+1} > \sqrt{n}$, it follows from inequalities (2) that

$$2\sqrt{n} - 2 < 1 + \frac{1}{\sqrt{2}} + \frac{1}{\sqrt{3}} + \frac{1}{\sqrt{4}} + \ldots + \frac{1}{\sqrt{n}} < 2\sqrt{n} - 1. \qquad (3)$$

Making use of inequalities (3) we now easily find the integral part of the number

$$y = 1 + \frac{1}{\sqrt{2}} + \frac{1}{\sqrt{3}} + \frac{1}{\sqrt{4}} + \ldots + \frac{1}{\sqrt{1,000,000}}.$$

For this we let $n = 1,000,000$ in the inequalities (3) and we obtain

$$2\sqrt{1\,000\,000} - 2 <$$

$$< 1 + \frac{1}{\sqrt{2}} + \frac{1}{\sqrt{3}} + \cdots + \frac{1}{\sqrt{1,000,000}} < 2\sqrt{1,000,000} - 1,$$

or

$$1998 < y < 1999.$$

It follows that $[y] = 1998$.

<u>Problem 3.</u> <u>Prove the inequality</u>

$$x = \frac{1}{2} \cdot \frac{3}{4} \cdot \frac{5}{6} \cdots \frac{99}{100} < \frac{1}{10}.$$

S o l u t i o n. Let

$$y = \frac{2}{3} \cdot \frac{4}{5} \cdot \frac{6}{7} \cdots \frac{100}{101}.$$

As

$$\frac{1}{2} < \frac{2}{3}, \quad \frac{3}{4} < \frac{4}{5}, \quad \frac{5}{6} < \frac{6}{7}, \ldots, \frac{99}{100} < \frac{100}{101},$$

therefore $x < y$, and it follows that

$$x^2 < xy = \frac{1}{2} \cdot \frac{2}{3} \cdot \frac{3}{4} \cdot \frac{4}{5} \cdot \frac{5}{6} \cdot \frac{6}{7} \cdots \frac{99}{100} \cdot \frac{100}{101} = \frac{1}{101}.$$

Extracting the square root from both sides of the inequality we obtain

$$x < \frac{1}{\sqrt{101}} < 0.1.$$

Exercises

1. Prove the inequalities

$$2\sqrt{n+1} - 2\sqrt{m} < \frac{1}{\sqrt{m}} + \frac{1}{\sqrt{m+1}} + \cdots + \frac{1}{\sqrt{n}} < 2\sqrt{n} - 2\sqrt{m-1}.$$

2. Prove the inequalities

$$1800 < \frac{1}{\sqrt{10,000}} + \frac{1}{\sqrt{10,001}} + \cdots + \frac{1}{\sqrt{1,000,000}} < 1800.02.$$

3. Find $[50z]$, where

$$z = \frac{1}{\sqrt{10,000}} + \frac{1}{\sqrt{10,001}} + \dots + \frac{1}{\sqrt{1,000,000}} .$$

Answer. $[50z] = 90,000.$

4. Prove the following inequality by induction:

$$\frac{1}{2} \cdot \frac{3}{4} \cdot \frac{5}{6} \dots \frac{2n-1}{2n} < \frac{1}{\sqrt{3n+1}} .$$

5. Prove the inequality

$$\frac{1}{2} \cdot \frac{3}{4} \cdot \frac{5}{6} \dots \frac{99}{100} < \frac{1}{12} .$$

Let us now proceed to study certain important inequalities used for solving many problems.

From the inequality $(x_1 - x_2)^2 \geqslant 0$ it follows that $x_1^2 + x_2^2 \geqslant 2x_1x_2$, where the equality sign applies only when $x_1 = x_2$.

If x_1 and x_2 are positive, dividing both sides of the latter inequality by x_1x_2, yields

$$\frac{x_1}{x_2} + \frac{x_2}{x_1} \geqslant 2. \tag{4}$$

Making use of the inequality (4) it is easy to prove that the sum of two positive numbers is not less than 2, if their product equals unity.

Indeed, if $xy = 1$, then $y = \frac{1}{x}$. The inequality $x + y \geqslant 2$ (i.e. $x + \frac{1}{x} \geqslant 2$) follows from the inequality (4) when $x_1 = x$ and $x_2 = 1$.

Let us now prove the theorem.

T h e o r e m 1. <u>If the product of n positive numbers equals 1 their sum is not less than n.</u>

In other words, it follows from the equality $x_1x_2x_3 \ldots x_n = 1$ that $x_1 + x_2 + x_3 + \ldots + x_n \geqslant n$, but $x_1 + x_2 + x_3 + \ldots + x_n > n$, when $x_1, x_2, x_3, \ldots, x_n$ are not all the same.

P r o o f. We shall prove this theorem by the method of induction*.

Earlier we proved the truth of Theorem 1 for the case of two positive numbers $(n = 2)$.

---

*Details of the method can be found in the book "The Method of Mathematical Induction" (I.S. Sominskii) English translation, Pergamon Press (1961).

We suppose that the theorem is true for $n = k \geqslant 2$, i.e. that the inequality

$$x_1 + x_2 + x_3 + \ldots + x_k \geqslant k$$

holds if $x_1 x_2 x_3 \ldots x_k = 1$; we then prove the theorem for $n = k+1$ i.e. we prove that

$$x_1 + x_2 + x_3 + \ldots + x_k + x_{k+1} \geqslant k+1,$$

if $x_1 x_2 x_3 \ldots x_k x_{k+1} = 1$, while $x_1 > 0$, $x_2 > 0$, $x_3 > 0, \ldots x_k > 0$, $x_{k+1} > 0$.

First of all we note that if

$$x_1 x_2 x_3 \ldots x_k x_{k+1} = 1,$$

then two cases might occur:

(1) All factors x_1, x_2, x_3, ..., x_k, x_{k+1} are identical, i.e.

$$x_1 = x_2 = x_3 = \ldots = x_k = x_{k+1},$$

(2) Some factors are different.

In the first case all terms are equal to 1 and their sum equals $k+1$, i.e.

$$x_1 + x_2 + x_3 + \ldots + x_k + x_{k+1} = k+1.$$

In the second case among the terms of the product $x_1 x_2 \ldots x_k x_{k+1}$ there will be found numbers greater and also smaller than 1 (if all the terms were smaller than 1, the product would also be smaller than 1).

For instance, let $x_1 < 1$ and $x_{k+1} > 1$. We have

$$(x_1 x_{k+1}) x_2 x_3 \ldots x_k = 1.$$

Putting $y_1 = x_1 x_{k+1}$, we get

$$y_1 x_2 x_3 \ldots x_k = 1.$$

As the product of k positive numbers here equals 1 (according to our assumption) their sum is not less than k, i.e.

$$y_1 + x_2 + x_3 + \ldots + x_k \geqslant k.$$

But

$$
\begin{aligned}
x_1 + x_2 + x_3 + \ldots &+ x_k + x_{k+1} = \\
&= (y_1 + x_2 + x_3 + \ldots + x_k) + x_{k+1} - y_1 + x_1 \geqslant \\
&\geqslant k + x_{k+1} - y_1 + x_1 = (k+1) + x_{k+1} - y_1 + x_1 - 1.
\end{aligned}
$$

Remembering that $y_1 = x_1 x_{k+1}$, we get

$$
\begin{aligned}
x_1 + x_2 + x_3 + \ldots + x_k &+ x_{k+1} \geqslant \\
&\geqslant (k+1) + x_{k+1} - x_1 x_{k+1} + x_1 - 1 = \\
&= (k+1) + (x_{k+1} - 1)(1 - x_1).
\end{aligned}
$$

As $x_1 < 1$ and $x_{k+1} > 1$, then $(x_{k+1} - 1)(1 - x_1) > 0$, and it follows that

$$
\begin{aligned}
x_1 + x_2 + x_3 + \ldots + x_k &+ x_{k+1} \geqslant \\
&\geqslant (k+1) + (x_{k+1} - 1)(1 - x_1) > k + 1.
\end{aligned}
$$

Thus Theorem 1 is proved.

Problem 1. Prove, that if $x_1, x_2, x_3, \ldots, x_n$ are positive numbers

$$\frac{x_1}{x_2} + \frac{x_2}{x_3} + \ldots + \frac{x_{n-1}}{x_n} + \frac{x_n}{x_1} \geqslant n,$$

and the equality sign applies only when

$$x_1 = x_2 = x_3 = \ldots = x_n.$$

Solution. Since

$$\frac{x_1}{x_2} \cdot \frac{x_2}{x_3} \ldots \frac{x_{n-1}}{x_n} \cdot \frac{x_n}{x_1} = 1,$$

the inequality follows from Theorem 1. The equality sign applies only when

$$\frac{x_1}{x_2} = \frac{x_2}{x_3} = \ldots = \frac{x_{n-1}}{x_n} = \frac{x_n}{x_1} = 1,$$

i.e. when $x_1 = x_2 = x_3 = \ldots = x_n$.

<u>Problem 2.</u> <u>Prove the inequality</u>

$$\frac{x^2+2}{\sqrt{x^2+1}} > 2.$$

S o l u t i o n. We have

$$\frac{x^2+2}{\sqrt{x^2+1}} = \frac{x^2+1}{\sqrt{x^2+1}} + \frac{1}{\sqrt{x^2+1}} = \sqrt{x^2+1} + \frac{1}{\sqrt{x^2+1}}.$$

As the product of the terms in the right-hand side of the equation is equal to 1 their sum is not less than 2. The sign of equality occurs only when $x = 0$.

<u>Problem 3.</u> <u>Prove that for</u> $a > 1$

$$\log_{10} a + \log_a 10 \geqslant 2.$$

S o l u t i o n. As $\log_a 10 \, \log_{10} a = 1$, then

$$\log_{10} a + \log_a 10 = \log_{10} a + \frac{1}{\log_{10} a} \geqslant 2.$$

<u>Problem 4.</u> <u>Prove the inequality</u>

$$\frac{x^2}{1+x^4} \leqslant \frac{1}{2}.$$

S o l u t i o n. We have the equality

$$\frac{x^2}{1+x^4} = \frac{1}{\frac{1}{x^2}+x^2}.$$

Since $\frac{1}{x^2} \cdot x^2 = 1$, it follows that $\frac{1}{x^2} + x^2 \geqslant 2$, and so

$$\frac{1}{\frac{1}{x^2}+x^2} \leqslant \frac{1}{2}.$$

D e f i n i t i o n. The number $g = \sqrt[n]{x_1 x_2 \ldots x_n}$ is called the __geometric mean__ of the positive numbers $x_1, x_2, \ldots, x_n$, and the number $a = \dfrac{x_1 + x_2 + \ldots + x_n}{n}$ is called the __arithmetic mean__ of the same numbers.

T h e o r e m 2. __The geometric mean of positive numbers is not greater than the arithmetic mean of the same numbers.__

__If numbers__ $x_1, x_2, \ldots, x_n$ __are not all the same, the geometric mean of these numbers is smaller than their arithmetic mean.__

P r o o f. From the equation $g = \sqrt[n]{x_1 x_2 \ldots x_n}$ it follows that

$$1 = \sqrt[n]{\frac{x_1}{g} \frac{x_2}{g} \ldots \frac{x_n}{g}}, \text{ or } \frac{x_1}{g} \frac{x_2}{g} \ldots \frac{x_n}{g} = 1.$$

As the product of n positive numbers equals 1, then (Theorem 1) their sum is not less than n, i.e.

$$\frac{x_1}{g} + \frac{x_2}{g} + \ldots + \frac{x_n}{g} \geqslant n.$$

Multiplying both sides of the latter inequality by g, and dividing them by n, we get

$$a = \frac{x_1 + x_2 + \ldots + x_n}{n} \geqslant g.$$

We note that the equality takes place only when

$$\frac{x_1}{g} = \frac{x_2}{g} = \ldots = \frac{x_n}{g} = 1, \text{ i.e. } x_1 = x_2 = \ldots = x_n = g.$$

If the numbers $x_1, x_2, \ldots, x_n$ are not all the same,

$$a > g.$$

__Problem 5.__ __Find the rectangular parallelepiped with the largest volume, if the sum of the lengths of three mutually perpendicular edges is given.__

S o l u t i o n. Let $m = a + b + c$ be the sum of the lengths of edges, and $V = abc$ (the volume of the parallelepiped). Since

$$\sqrt[3]{V} = \sqrt[3]{abc} \leqslant \frac{a+b+c}{3} = \frac{m}{3},$$

then $V \leqslant \frac{m^3}{27}$. The sign of equality applies only when $a = b = c = \frac{m}{3}$, i.e. when the parallelepiped is a cube.

Problem 6. Prove the inequality

$$n! < \left(\frac{n+1}{2}\right)^n, \quad n \geqslant 2. \tag{5}$$

S o l u t i o n. Using Theorem 2 we get

$$\sqrt[n]{n!} = \sqrt[n]{1 \cdot 2 \cdot 3 \ldots n} < \frac{1 + 2 + 3 + \ldots + n}{n} =$$
$$= \frac{(n+1)n}{2n} = \frac{n+1}{2}.$$

Raising both sides of the last inequality to the nth power we obtain the inequality (5).

D e f i n i t i o n s. The number

$$c_a = \left(\frac{a_1^a + a_2^a + \ldots + a_n^a}{n}\right)^{\frac{1}{a}}$$

is called the exponential mean of order α of the numbers $a_1, a_2, \ldots, a_n$. In particular, the number

$$c_1 = \frac{a_1 + a_2 + \ldots + a_n}{n}$$

is the arithmetic mean of numbers $a_1, a_2, \ldots, a_n$, the number

$$c_2 = \left(\frac{a_1^2 + a_2^2 + \ldots + a_n^2}{n}\right)^{\frac{1}{2}}$$

is called the quadratic mean, and the number

$$c_{-1} = \left(\frac{a_1^{-1} + a_2^{-1} + \ldots + a_n^{-1}}{n}\right)^{-1} = \frac{n}{\frac{1}{a_1} + \frac{1}{a_2} + \ldots + \frac{1}{a_n}}$$

is called the <u>harmonic mean</u> of the numbers a_1, a_2, ..., a_n.

<u>Problem 7</u>. <u>Prove that if a_1, a_2, ..., a_n are positive numbers</u>
<u>and $\alpha < 0 < \beta$</u>,

$$c_\alpha \leqslant g \leqslant c_\beta, \tag{6}$$

<u>i.e. the exponential mean with a negative index is not grea-</u>
<u>ter than the geometric mean, and the exponential mean with a</u>
<u>positive index is not less than the geometric mean.</u>

S o l u t i o n. Making use of the fact that the geometric
mean of positive numbers does not exceed their arithmetic
mean we have

$$\sqrt[n]{a_1^\alpha a_3^\alpha \ldots a_n^\alpha} \leqslant \frac{a_1^\alpha + a_2^\alpha + \ldots + a_n^\alpha}{n}.$$

Raising both sides of the last inequality to the power $\frac{1}{\alpha}$,

and remembering that $\frac{1}{\alpha} < 0$, we obtain

$$g = \sqrt[n]{a_1 a_2 \ldots a_n} \geqslant \left(\frac{a_1^\alpha + a_3^\alpha + \ldots + a_n^\alpha}{n}\right)^{\frac{1}{\alpha}} = c_\alpha.$$

Thus, the first part of the inequality (6) is proved. The
second part can be proved similarly.

It follows from the inequality (6) that, in particular, the
harmonic mean c_{-1} does not exceed the arithmetic mean c_1.

<u>Problem 8</u>. <u>Prove that if a_1, a_3, ..., a_n are positive numbers,</u>

$$(a_1 + a_2 + \ldots + a_n)\left(\frac{1}{a_1} + \frac{1}{a_2} + \ldots + \frac{1}{a_n}\right) \geqslant n^2.$$

S o l u t i o n. As $c_{-1} \leqslant g \leqslant c_1$

$$c_{-1} = \frac{n}{\frac{1}{a_1} + \frac{1}{a_2} + \ldots + \frac{1}{a_n}} \leqslant \frac{a_1 + a_2 + \ldots + a_n}{n} = c_1.$$

It follows from this inequality that

$$n^2 \leqslant (a_1 + a_2 + \ldots + a_n)\left(\frac{1}{a_1} + \frac{1}{a_2} + \ldots + \frac{1}{a_n}\right).$$

Problem 9. <u>Prove that for any positive numbers *a*, *b* $(a \neq b)$ the following inequality holds</u>

$$\sqrt[n+1]{ab^n} < \frac{a + nb}{n+1}.$$

S o l u t i o n. We have

$$\sqrt[n+1]{ab^n} = \sqrt[n+1]{a\underbrace{bb\ldots b}_{n}} < \frac{a + \overbrace{\frac{b + b + \ldots + b}{n}}^{}}{n+1} = \frac{a + nb}{n+1},$$

as was required.

Problem 10. <u>Prove that the quantities</u>

$$x_n = \left(1 + \frac{1}{n}\right)^n \text{ and } z_n = \left(1 - \frac{1}{n}\right)^n$$

<u>increase as *n* increases</u>, i.e.

$$x_n < x_{n+1} = \left(1 + \frac{1}{n+1}\right)^{n+1}, \quad z_n < z_{n+1} = \left(1 - \frac{1}{n+1}\right)^{n+1}.$$

S o l u t i o n. Putting $a = 1, b = 1 + \frac{1}{n}$, in the inequality of the previous problem, we obtain

$$\sqrt[n+1]{1 \cdot \left(1 + \frac{1}{n}\right)^n} < \frac{1 + n\left(1 + \frac{1}{n}\right)}{n+1} = \frac{n+2}{n+1} = 1 + \frac{1}{n+1}.$$

Raising both sides of the inequality to the $(n+1)$th power, we have

$$\left(1 + \frac{1}{n}\right)^n < \left(1 + \frac{1}{n+1}\right)^{n+1}, \text{ i.e. } x_n < x_{n+1}.$$

The second inequality is proved similarly.

Problem 11. Prove that
$$y_n = \left(1 + \frac{1}{n}\right)^{n+1}$$
decreases with increase of the number n, i.e.

$$y_n > y_{n+1} = \left(1 + \frac{1}{n+1}\right)^{n+2}.$$

S o l u t i o n. We have

$$y_n = \left(1 + \frac{1}{n}\right)^{n+1} = \left(\frac{n+1}{n}\right)^{n+1} = \frac{1}{\left(\frac{n}{n+1}\right)^{n+1}} =$$

$$= \frac{1}{\left(1 - \frac{1}{n+1}\right)^{n+1}} = \frac{1}{z_{n+1}}$$

(with notation of Problem 10). Since z_n increases with the increase of the number n, it follows that y_n decreases.

In Problems 10 and 11 we proved that

$$x_1 = \left(1 + \frac{1}{1}\right)^1 = 2 < x_2 =$$
$$= \left(1 + \frac{1}{2}\right)^2 = 2.25 < x_3 < \ldots < x_n < \ldots,$$
$$y_1 = \left(1 + \frac{1}{1}\right)^2 = 4 > y_2 =$$
$$= \left(1 + \frac{1}{2}\right)^3 = 3.375 > y_3 > \ldots > y_n > \ldots$$

On the other hand

$$2 = x_1 < x_n = \left(1 + \frac{1}{n}\right)^n < \left(1 + \frac{1}{n}\right)^{n+1} = v_n < v_1 = 4.$$

And so the variable quantity x_n satisfies two conditions:

(1) x_n increases monotonically with the increase of the number n.

(2) x_n is a bounded quantity $2 < x_n < 4$.

It is known from elementary analysis that a variable quantity, which is bounded and increases monotonically, tends to

S o l u t i o n.   Since $\sin 2x = 2 \sin x \cos x$, we have

$$\sin x \sin 2x = 2 \cos x \sin^2 x = 2 \cos x (1 - \cos^2 x) = 2 (z - z^3),$$

where $z = \cos x$, and consequently $-1 \leqslant z \leqslant 1$. The function $z - z^3$ $= z (1 - z^2)$ has a negative value if $-1 \leqslant z < 0$ and for $0 \leqslant z \leqslant 1$ it takes a positive value.

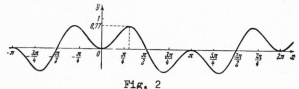

Fig. 2

It follows that the greatest value of the function is achieved in the interval $0 < z \leqslant 1$.

In Problem 1 it was shown, that the function $z - z^3$, $z \geqslant 0$ takes its greatest value at the point

$$z = \left(\frac{1}{3}\right)^{\frac{1}{3-1}} = \frac{1}{\sqrt{3}}.$$

At this point

$$\sin x \sin 2x = 2z (1 - z^2) = \frac{2}{\sqrt{3}} \left(1 - \frac{1}{3}\right) = \frac{4}{3\sqrt{3}}.$$

Thus, the function $y = \sin x \sin 2x$ takes its greatest value at those points at which $z = \cos x = \frac{1}{\sqrt{3}}$, and this value is $\frac{4}{3\sqrt{3}}$. The graph of the function $y = \sin x \sin 2x$ is represented in Fig. 2

Problem 4.   Find the greatest value of the function

$$y = \cos x \cos 2x.$$

S o l u t i o n.   The function $y = \cos x \cos 2x$ does not exceed 1, as neither of the factors $\cos x$ and $\cos 2x$ exceeds 1.   But at the points $x = 0, \pm 2\pi, \pm 4\pi, \ldots$

$$\cos x \cos 2x = 1.$$

Thus, the function $y = \cos x \cos 2x$ takes its greatest value = 1 at the points $x = 0, \pm 2\pi, \pm 4\pi, ..$ The graph of the function $y = \cos x \cos 2x$ is represented in Fig. 3.

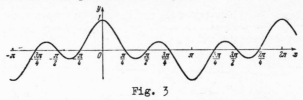

Fig. 3

Problem 5. <u>Find the least value of the function</u>

$$x^{\alpha} + ax,$$

<u>where</u> $a > 0$, $\alpha < 0$, $x \geqslant 0$.

S o l u t i o n. Since $\alpha < 0$, then, in accordance with the inequality (12),

$$(1 + z)^{\alpha} \geqslant 1 + \alpha z,$$

where the equality sign applies only when $z = 0$. Putting $1 + z = y$, $z = y - 1$, we get

$$y^{\alpha} \geqslant 1 + \alpha(y - 1), \quad y \geqslant 0,$$

where the equality sign applies only when $y = 1$. From the last inequality it follows that

$$y^{\alpha} - \alpha y \geqslant 1 - \alpha, \quad (cy)^{\alpha} - \alpha c^{\alpha - 1}(cy) \geqslant (1 - \alpha) c^{\alpha}.$$

Putting $a = -\alpha c^{\alpha - 1}$, $x = cy$, we get

$$x^{\alpha} + ax \geqslant (1 - \alpha) c^{\alpha} = (1 - \alpha)\left(\frac{a}{-\alpha}\right)^{\frac{\alpha}{\alpha - 1}},$$

where the equality sign takes place only when $x = c = \left(\frac{a}{-\alpha}\right)^{\frac{1}{\alpha - 1}}$.

Thus, the function $x^{\alpha} + ax$ takes on its least value at the point $x = \left(\frac{a}{-\alpha}\right)^{\frac{1}{\alpha - 1}}$, that value being equal to

$$(1 - \alpha)\left(\frac{a}{-\alpha}\right)^{\frac{\alpha}{\alpha - 1}}.$$

For example, the function

$$\frac{1}{\sqrt[3]{x}} + 27x, \quad x \geqslant 0$$

takes on the least value at the point

$$x = \left(\frac{27}{\frac{1}{3}}\right)^{-\frac{1}{-\frac{1}{3}-1}} = \frac{1}{27}.$$

This value equals

$$\left(1 + \frac{1}{3}\right)\left(\frac{27}{\frac{1}{3}}\right)^{-\frac{\frac{1}{3}}{-\frac{1}{3}-1}} = 4.$$

Problem 6. Find the most convenient dimensions of a cy-
lindrical vessel with a bottom and a lid*.

S o l u t i o n. Let $V = \pi r^2 h$ be the volume of the vessel,
where r is the radius, h the height of the cylinder. The
full surface of the vessel has an area

$$S = 2\pi r^2 + 2\pi r h.$$

Since $h = \frac{V}{\pi r^2}$, then

$$S = 2\pi r^2 + 2\pi r \frac{V}{\pi r^2} = 2\pi r^2 + \frac{2V}{r}.$$

Putting $x = \frac{1}{r}$ we get

$$S = 2\pi x^{-2} + 2Vx = 2\pi \left(x^{-2} + \frac{V}{\pi} x\right).$$

According to the solution of the previous problem the function $x^{-2} + \frac{V}{\pi} x$ takes its least value when

---

* The dimensions of a vessel are regarded as most convenient
if for a given volume the least amount of material is required for its manufacture, i.e. the vessel has the least
surface area.

$$x = \left(\frac{V}{2\pi}\right)^{-\frac{1}{-2-1}} = \sqrt[3]{\frac{2\pi}{V}}.$$

Returning to our previous notation we find:

$$\frac{1}{r} = \sqrt[3]{\frac{2\pi}{V}}, \quad r^3 = \frac{V}{2\pi} = \frac{\pi r^2 h}{2\pi}, \quad r = \frac{h}{2}, \quad h = 2r = d.$$

Thus, the vessel has most convenient dimensions when its height and its diameter are equal.

Exercises

6. Find the greatest value of the function $x(6-x)^2$ when $0 < x < 6$.

H i n t: Put $v = 6 - x$.

7. From a square sheet of side $2a$ a box without a lid is made by cutting off squares from the corners of the sheet and bending up the projections thus formed. The volume of the box is to have the greatest possible volume. Find the length of the side of the squares cut out.

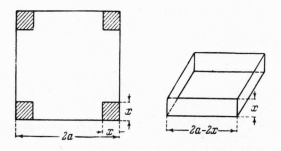

Fig. 4

8. Find the least value of the function

$$x^6 + 8x^2 + 5.$$

9. Find the least value of the function

$$x^6 - 8x^2 + 5.$$

10. Find the greatest value of the function

$$x^n - ax,$$

when $0 < a < 1$, $a > 0$, $x > 0$.

11. Prove the inequality

$$\sqrt[4]{x} \leqslant \frac{3}{8} + 2x.$$

12. Prove that for $n > 3$ the following inequality holds

$$\sqrt[n]{n} > \sqrt[n+1]{n+1}.$$

H i n t: Use inequality (7).

13. Find the greatest of the numbers

$$1, \ \sqrt{2}, \ \sqrt[3]{3}, \ \sqrt[4]{4}, \ \sqrt[5]{5}, \ldots, \ \sqrt[n]{n}, \ldots$$

14. Prove the inequality

$$\sqrt[n]{n} < 1 + \frac{2}{\sqrt{n}}.$$

15. Prove the inequality

$$(1 + a_1)(1 + a_2)\ldots(1 + a_n) > 1 + a_1 + a_2 + \ldots + a_n,$$

if the numbers a_i are of the same sign and not less than -1.

16. Prove the inequality

$$(a_1b_1 + a_2b_2 + \ldots + a_nb_n)^2 \leqslant$$
$$\leqslant (a_1^2 + a_2^2 + \ldots + a_n^2)(b_1^2 + b_2^2 + \ldots + b_n^2). \tag{19}$$

H i n t: First prove that the polynomial

$$(a_1x - b_1)^2 + (a_2x - b_2)^2 + \ldots + (a_nx - b_n)^2 =$$
$$= x^2(a_1^2 + a_2^2 + \ldots + a_n^2) - 2x(a_1b_1 + a_2b_2 + \ldots + a_nb_n +$$
$$+ (b_1^2 + b_2^2 + \ldots + b_n^2)$$

cannot have two different real roots.

17. Using the inequality (19) prove that the arithmetic mean is not greater than the quadratic mean.

18. Prove the inequality

$$\frac{1}{\sqrt{n}} < \sqrt{n+1} - \sqrt{n-1}.$$

19. Using the inequality in Problem 18 prove the inequality

$$\sqrt{n+1} + \sqrt{n} - \sqrt{2} > 1 + \frac{1}{\sqrt{2}} + \frac{1}{\sqrt{3}} + \ldots + \frac{1}{\sqrt{n}}.$$

20. Find the greatest values of the functions

$$\frac{x^3}{x^4 + 5}, \quad x^6 - 0.6x^{10}.$$

A n s w e r: $\frac{3}{4\sqrt[4]{15}}$; 0.4.

21. For what value of a does the least value of the function $\sqrt{x} + \frac{a}{x^2}$ equal 2.5?

A n s w e r: $a = 8$.

5. APPLICATION TO THE CALCULATION OF SOME LIMITS

In this section we shall examine a few important inequalities and shall indicate their application to the calculation of certain limits.

Problem 1.   Prove that if $p > 1$, $\frac{1}{p} + \frac{1}{q} = 1$, $x > 0$, $y > 0$, then

$$xy \leqslant \frac{x^p}{p} + \frac{y^q}{q}. \tag{20}$$

S o l u t i o n.   At the beginning of Section 4 (Problem 1) we proved the inequality

$$x^\alpha - ax \geqslant (1 - \alpha)\left(\frac{a}{\alpha}\right)^{\frac{\alpha}{\alpha - 1}},$$

when $\alpha > 1$, $a > 0$, $x \geqslant 0$.

Putting $\alpha = p$, $a = py$ in this inequality we get

$$x^p - (py)\,x \geqslant (1 - p)\left(\frac{py}{p}\right)^{\frac{p}{p-1}} = (1 - p)\,y^{\frac{p}{p-1}}. \tag{21}$$

As $\frac{1}{p} + \frac{1}{q} = 1$, then

$$\frac{1}{q} = 1 - \frac{1}{p} = \frac{p-1}{p}, \quad q = \frac{p}{p-1}, \quad p - 1 = \frac{p}{q}.$$

Substituting these values in the inequality (21) we obtain

$$x^p - pyx \geqslant -\frac{p}{q}\,y^q.$$

Dividing the last inequality throughout by p and transferring all the negative terms to the opposite side, we obtain the inequality (20).

Problem 2. <u>Prove that if a_1, a_2, ..., a_n. b_1, b_2, ..., b_n are posi-tive numbers, and p and q satisfy the conditions laid down in problem 1,</u>

$$(a_1b_1 + a_2b_2 + \ldots + a_nb_n) \leqslant$$
$$\leqslant (a_1^p + a_2^p + \ldots + a_n^p)^{\frac{1}{p}} (b_1^q + b_2^q + \ldots + b_n^q)^{\frac{1}{q}}. \tag{22}$$

S o l u t i o n. Let

$$a_1^p + a_2^p + \ldots + a_n^p = A^p, \quad b_1^q + b_2^q + \ldots + b_n^q = B^q.$$

Then the right-hand side of the inequality (22) is equal to

$$(A^p)^{\frac{1}{p}} (B^q)^{\frac{1}{q}} = AB.$$

Now let

$$a_1 = Ac_1, \quad a_2 = Ac_2, \ldots, \quad a_n = Ac_n,$$
$$b_1 = Bd_1, \quad b_2 = Bd_2, \ldots, \quad b_n = Bd_n.$$

Since

$$A^p = a_1^p + a_2^p + \ldots + a_n^p = A^p c_1^p + A^p c_2^p + \ldots + A^p c_n^p =$$
$$= A^p (c_1^p + c_2^p + \ldots + c_n^p),$$

we have

$$c_1^p + c_2^p + \ldots + c_n^p = 1.$$

In the same way it can be verified that

$$d_1^q + d_2^q + \ldots + d_n^q = 1.$$

Making use of the inequalities,

$$\left. \begin{aligned} a_1b_1 &= AB(c_1d_1) \leqslant AB \left(\frac{c_1^p}{p} + \frac{d_1^q}{q} \right), \\ a_2b_2 &\leqslant AB \left(\frac{c_2^p}{p} + \frac{d_2^q}{q} \right), \end{aligned} \right\} \tag{*}$$

$$a_n b_n \leqslant AB \left(\frac{c_n^p}{p} + \frac{d_n^q}{q} \right). \qquad \Big|$$

From these inequalities it follows that

$$a_1 b_1 + a_2 b_2 + \ldots + a_n b_n \leqslant$$

$$\leqslant AB \left(\frac{c_1^p + c_2^p + \ldots + c_n^p}{p} + \frac{d_1^q + d_2^q + \ldots + d_n^q}{q} \right) =$$

$$= AB \left(\frac{1}{p} + \frac{1}{q} \right) = AB$$

(we remember that $\frac{1}{p} + \frac{1}{q} = 1$, $c_1^p + c_2^p + \ldots + c_n^p = 1$, $d_1^q + d_2^q + \ldots + d_n^q = 1$).

And so, it has been proved that the left-hand side of the inequality (22) does not exceed AB, i.e. does not exceed the right-hand side.

It is easy to point out the case when the sign of equality occurs in (22). Indeed, the sign of equality occurs in (21) only when

$$x = \left(\frac{py}{p} \right)^{\frac{1}{p-1}} = y^{\frac{1}{p-1}} = y^{\frac{q}{p}}, \quad x^p = y^q$$

(see Problem 1 in Section 4). In the same way, in each line of (*) the sign of equality occurs only when

$$c_1 = d_1^{\frac{q}{p}}, \quad c_2 = d_2^{\frac{q}{p}}, \ldots, \quad c_n = d_n^{\frac{q}{p}},$$

i.e. when

$$c_1^p = d_1^q, \quad c_2^p = d_2^q, \ldots, \quad c_n^p = d_n^q.$$

Finally, multiplying these equations by $A^p B^q$ we get:

$$B^q (Ac_1)^p = A^p (Bd_1)^q, \text{ i.e. } B^q a_1^p = A^p b_1^q,$$

$$\frac{a_1^p}{b_1^q} = \frac{A^p}{B^q}, \quad \frac{a_2^p}{b_2^q} = \frac{A^p}{B^q}, \ldots, \quad \frac{a_n^p}{b_n^q} = \frac{A^p}{B^q}.$$

Thus, the sign of equality in (22) occurs if

$$\frac{a_1^p}{b_1^q} = \frac{a_2^p}{b_2^q} = \ldots = \frac{a_n^p}{b_n^q}.$$

N o t e. Putting $p = 2$, $q = 2$, in the inequality (22) we obtain the inequality (19) (see Exercise 16).

$$a_1 b_1 + a_2 b_2 + \ldots + a_n b_n \leqslant$$
$$\leqslant \sqrt{(a_1^2 + a_2^2 + \ldots + a_n^2)(b_1^2 + b_2^2 + \ldots + b_n^2)}.$$

Problem 3. <u>Prove the inequality</u>

$$\frac{1}{n+1} < \ln\left(1 + \frac{1}{n}\right) < \frac{1}{n} \ ). \ * \tag{23}$$

S o l u t i o n. Combining the inequalities (7) and (8) in Section 2 we obtain

$$\left(1 + \frac{1}{n}\right)^n < e < \left(1 + \frac{1}{n}\right)^{n+1}.$$

Taking logarithms of these inequalities to the base e, we finally find that

$$n \ln\left(1 + \frac{1}{n}\right) < \ln e = 1 < (n+1)\ln\left(1 + \frac{1}{n}\right),$$

that is

$$\frac{1}{n+1} < \ln\left(1 + \frac{1}{n}\right) < \frac{1}{n}.$$

Problem 4. <u>If</u> $z_1 = 1 + \frac{1}{2}$, $z_2 = \frac{1}{2} + \frac{1}{3} + \frac{1}{4}$,
$z_3 = \frac{1}{3} + \frac{1}{4} + \frac{1}{5} + \frac{1}{6}$, $z_4 = \frac{1}{4} + \frac{1}{5} + \frac{1}{6} + \frac{1}{7} + \frac{1}{8}, \ldots$
$\ldots, z_n = \frac{1}{n} + \frac{1}{n+1} + \frac{1}{n+2} + \ldots + \frac{1}{2n},$

<u>find</u> $\lim\limits_{n \to \infty} z_n$.

S o l u t i o n. Substituting $n - 1$ for n in the first part of the inequality (23) we obtain:

$$\frac{1}{n} < \ln\left(1 + \frac{1}{n-1}\right) = \ln \frac{n}{n-1}.$$

---

* $\ln\left(1 + \frac{1}{n}\right)$ means the logarithm of $\left(1 + \frac{1}{n}\right)$ to the base e; see

p. 15 above.

From this inequality and the second part of the inequality (23) it follows that:

$$\ln \frac{n+1}{n} < \frac{1}{n} < \ln \frac{n}{n-1}.$$ (24)

Now, making use of the inequalities (24) we have the inequalities

$$\ln \frac{n+1}{n} < \frac{1}{n} < \ln \frac{n}{n-1},$$

$$\ln \frac{n+2}{n+1} < \frac{1}{n+1} < \ln \frac{n+1}{n},$$

$$\ln \frac{n+3}{n+2} < \frac{1}{n+2} < \ln \frac{n+2}{n+1},$$

$$\cdots \cdots \cdots \cdots \cdots$$

$$\ln \frac{2n+1}{2n} < \frac{1}{2n} < \ln \frac{2n}{2n-1}.$$

Adding them and taking into account that the sum of logarithms is equal to the logarithm of the product, we obtain:

$$\ln \frac{(n+1)(n+2)(n+3)\ldots(2n+1)}{n(n+1)(n+2)\ldots 2n} <$$
$$< \frac{1}{n} + \frac{1}{n+1} + \cdots + \frac{1}{2n} < \ln \frac{n(n+1)(n+2)\ldots 2n}{(n-1)n(n+1)\ldots(2n-1)},$$

i.e.

$$\ln \frac{2n+1}{n} < \frac{1}{n} + \frac{1}{n+1} + \cdots + \frac{1}{2n} < \ln \frac{2n}{n-1}.$$ (25)

Since $\frac{2n+1}{n} = 2 + \frac{1}{n}$, we then have

$$\lim_{n \to \infty} \ln \frac{2n+1}{n} = \lim_{n \to \infty} \ln\left(2 + \frac{1}{n}\right) = \ln 2.$$

Exactly in the same way, it follows from $\frac{2n}{n-1} = 2 + \frac{2}{n-1}$ that

$$\lim_{n \to \infty} \ln \frac{2n}{n-1} = \ln 2.$$

Thus, the outer parts of the inequalities (25) have identical limits. Consequently, the middle part also has the same limit, i.e.

$$\lim_{n \to \infty} \left(\frac{1}{n} + \frac{1}{n+1} + \cdots + \frac{1}{2n} \right) = \lim_{n \to \infty} z_n = \ln 2.$$

Problem 5. If

$$x_1 = 1, \quad x_2 = 1 - \frac{1}{2}, \quad x_3 = 1 - \frac{1}{2} + \frac{1}{3}, \ldots$$

$$\ldots, x_n = 1 - \frac{1}{2} + \frac{1}{3} - \frac{1}{4} + \frac{1}{5} - \frac{1}{6} + \cdots + (-1)^{n-1} \frac{1}{n},$$

calculate $\lim_{n \to \infty} x_n$.

S o l u t i o n. We have

$$x_{2n} = 1 - \frac{1}{2} + \frac{1}{3} - \frac{1}{4} + \frac{1}{5} - \frac{1}{6} + \cdots + \frac{1}{2n-1} - \frac{1}{2n} =$$
$$= \left(1 + \frac{1}{2} + \frac{1}{3} + \frac{1}{4} + \frac{1}{5} + \frac{1}{6} + \cdots + \frac{1}{2n-1} + \frac{1}{2n} \right) -$$
$$- 2 \left(\frac{1}{2} + \frac{1}{4} + \frac{1}{6} + \cdots + \frac{1}{2n} \right) =$$
$$= \left(1 + \frac{1}{2} + \frac{1}{3} + \frac{1}{4} + \frac{1}{5} + \frac{1}{6} + \cdots + \frac{1}{2n-1} + \frac{1}{2n} \right) -$$
$$- \left(1 + \frac{1}{2} + \frac{1}{3} + \cdots + \frac{1}{n} \right) =$$
$$= \frac{1}{n+1} + \frac{1}{n+2} + \cdots + \frac{1}{2n}.$$

In the preceding problem we put

$$z_n = \frac{1}{n} + \frac{1}{n+1} + \cdots + \frac{1}{2n}.$$

Consequently $x_{2n} = z_n - \frac{1}{n}$. But $\lim_{n \to \infty} z_n = \ln 2$ (see the preceding problem). Thus

$$\lim_{n \to \infty} x_{2n} = \lim_{n \to \infty} \left(z_n - \frac{1}{n} \right) = \ln 2.$$

In addition we note that $x_{2n+1} = x_{2n} + \frac{1}{2n+1}$ and, consequently, that

$$\lim_{n \to \infty} x_{2n+1} = \lim_{n \to \infty} \left(x_{2n} + \frac{1}{2n+1} \right) = \ln 2.$$

And so

$$\lim_{n \to \infty} x_n = \ln 2.$$

N o t e. The numbers $x_1 = a_1$, $x_2 = a_1 + a_2$, $x_3 = a_1 + a_2 + a_3$, ..., $x_n = a_1 + a_2 + ... + a_n$ are called partial sums of the series

$$a_1 + a_2 + a_3 + ... + a_n + ...$$

The series is said to be <u>convergent</u> if the sequence of its partial sums has a finite limit. In this case the number

$S = \lim\limits_{n \to \infty} x_n$ is called the sum of the series. From Problem 5

it follows that the series

$$1 - \frac{1}{2} + \frac{1}{3} - \frac{1}{4} + \frac{1}{5} - \frac{1}{6} + ... + \frac{1}{2n-1} - \frac{1}{2n} + ...$$

is convergent and has its sum $\ln 2$.

<u>Problem 6.</u> <u>The series</u>

$$1 + \frac{1}{2} + \frac{1}{3} + \frac{1}{4} + ... + \frac{1}{n} + ...$$

<u>is called the harmonic series. Prove that the harmonic series</u>
<u>is divergent.</u>

S o l u t i o n. From inequality (23)

$$\frac{1}{n} > \ln \frac{n+1}{n}.$$

Putting $n = 1, 2, 3, ..., n$ we have n inequalities

$$1 > \ln \frac{2}{1},$$
$$\frac{1}{2} > \ln \frac{3}{2},$$
$$\frac{1}{3} > \ln \frac{4}{3},$$
$$. . . . . .$$
$$\frac{1}{n} > \ln \frac{n+1}{n}.$$

Adding them we get

$$x_n = 1 + \frac{1}{2} + \frac{1}{3} + \ldots + \frac{1}{n} >$$
$$> \ln \frac{2 \cdot 3 \cdot 4 \ldots (n+1)}{1 \cdot 2 \cdot 3 \ldots n} = \ln(n+1).$$

From this inequality it follows that

$$\lim_{n \to \infty} x_n \geqslant \lim_{n \to \infty} \ln(n+1) = \infty,$$

It follows that the harmonic series diverges.

Problem 7. **Prove that the series**

$$1 + \frac{1}{2^\alpha} + \frac{1}{3^\alpha} + \ldots + \frac{1}{n^\alpha} + \ldots \qquad (26)$$

converges for any $\alpha > 1$.

S o l u t i o n. The sequence of partial sums of this series

$$x_1 = 1,$$
$$x_2 = 1 + \frac{1}{2^\alpha},$$
$$x_3 = 1 + \frac{1}{2^\alpha} + \frac{1}{3^\alpha},$$
$$x_4 = 1 + \frac{1}{2^\alpha} + \frac{1}{3^\alpha} + \frac{1}{4^\alpha},$$
$$\ldots \ldots \ldots \ldots \ldots \ldots$$
$$x_n = 1 + \frac{1}{2^\alpha} + \frac{1}{3^\alpha} + \ldots + \frac{1}{n^\alpha}$$

increases monotonically, i.e.

$$x_1 < x_2 < x_3 < x_4 < \ldots < x_n < \ldots$$

On the other hand, it is known that a monotonically increasing bounded sequence has a finite limit. Consequently, if we prove that the sequence of numbers x_n is bounded, the convergence of the series (26) will also be proved.

Suppose

$$y_{2n} = 1 - \frac{1}{2^a} + \frac{1}{3^a} - \frac{1}{4^a} + \frac{1}{5^a} - \frac{1}{6^a} + \ldots + \frac{1}{(2n-1)^a} - \frac{1}{(2n)^a}.$$

Since

$$y_{2n} = 1 - \left(\frac{1}{2^a} - \frac{1}{3^a}\right) - \left(\frac{1}{4^a} - \frac{1}{5^a}\right) - \ldots -$$
$$- \left(\frac{1}{(2n-2)^a} - \frac{1}{(2n-1)^a}\right) - \frac{1}{(2n)^a},$$

we have (the numbers in each pair of brackets being positive)

$$y_{2n} < 1.$$

On the other hand,

$$y_{2n} = 1 - \frac{1}{2^a} + \frac{1}{3^a} - \frac{1}{4^a} + \frac{1}{5^a} - \frac{1}{6^a} + \ldots +$$
$$+ \frac{1}{(2n-1)^a} - \frac{1}{(2n)^a} = \left(1 + \frac{1}{2^a} + \frac{1}{3^a} + \frac{1}{4^a} + \frac{1}{5^a} +\right.$$
$$+ \frac{1}{6^a} + \ldots + \frac{1}{(2n-1)^a} + \frac{1}{(2n)^a}\right) -$$
$$- 2\left(\frac{1}{2^a} + \frac{1}{4^a} + \frac{1}{6^a} + \ldots + \frac{1}{(2n)^a}\right) =$$
$$= \left(1 + \frac{1}{2^a} + \frac{1}{3^a} + \frac{1}{4^a} + \frac{1}{5^a} + \frac{1}{6^a} + \ldots +\right.$$
$$+ \frac{1}{(2n-1)^a} + \frac{1}{(2n)^a}\right) - \frac{2}{2^a}\left(1 + \frac{1}{2^a} + \frac{1}{3^a} + \ldots + \frac{1}{n^a}\right).$$

Since $x_n = 1 + \frac{1}{2^a} + \frac{1}{3^a} + \ldots + \frac{1}{n^a}$,

$$y_{2n} = x_{2n} - \frac{2}{2^a} x_n.$$

Now, as $x_{2n} > x_n$, $y_{2n} < 1$ it follows that

$$1 > y_{2n} > x_n - \frac{2}{2^a} x_n = \frac{2^a - 2}{2^a} x_n,$$

and hence that

$$x_n < \frac{2^a}{2^a - 2},$$

i.e. the numbers x_n are bounded when $a > 1$. By this it is proved that the series (26) is convergent and that its sum is not greater than $\frac{2^a}{2^a - 2}$.

For instance, if $\alpha = 2$, then

$$x_n = 1 + \frac{1}{2^2} + \frac{1}{3^2} + \ldots + \frac{1}{n^2} < \frac{2^2}{2^2 - 2} = 2,$$

$$S = \lim_{n \to \infty} x_n = 1 + \frac{1}{2^2} + \frac{1}{3^2} + \ldots + \frac{1}{n^2} + \ldots \leqslant 2.$$

In the course of studying higher mathematics (e.g. in Fourier series) we find that

$$S = 1 + \frac{1}{2^2} + \frac{1}{3^2} + \ldots + \frac{1}{n^2} + \ldots = \frac{\pi^2}{6}. \tag{27}$$

Exercises

22. Find the sum of the series

$$S = 1 - \frac{1}{2^2} + \frac{1}{3^2} - \frac{1}{4^2} + \ldots + (-1)^{n-1} \frac{1}{n^2} + \ldots$$

H i n t: Use the equation (27)

A n s w e r. $S = \frac{\pi^2}{12}$.

23. Prove the inequalities

$$\frac{n^{\alpha+1}}{\alpha+1} < 1 + 2^\alpha + 3^\alpha + \ldots + n^\alpha < \frac{(n+1)^{\alpha+1}}{\alpha+1} \qquad \alpha > 0.$$

24. If

$$x_n = 1 + 2^\alpha + 3^\alpha + \ldots + n^\alpha,$$

prove that

$$\lim_{n \to \infty} \frac{x_n}{n^{\alpha+1}} = \frac{1}{\alpha+1}, \qquad \alpha > 0.$$

25. Prove the inequality

$$(a_1 b_1 c_1 + a_2 b_2 c_2 + \ldots + a_n b_n c_n)^3 \leqslant$$
$$\leqslant (a_1^3 + a_2^3 + \ldots + a_n^3)(b_1^3 + b_2^3 + \ldots + b_n^3)(c_1^3 + c_2^3 + \ldots + c_n^3),$$

if the numbers a_i, b_k, c_k are positive.

H i n t: Make use of the inequality (10) and of the method of proof in (22).

26. If $x_n = \dfrac{1}{n} + \dfrac{1}{n+1} + \dfrac{1}{n+2} + \ldots + \dfrac{1}{kn}$, where k is a whole positive number, prove that

$$\lim_{n \to \infty} x_n = \ln k.$$

H i n t: Make use of the method used in solving Problem 4 of the present chapter.

1. In the inequalities (1) (page 2) we put $n = m, m+1, \ldots, n$:

$$2\sqrt{m+1} - 2\sqrt{m} < \frac{1}{\sqrt{m}} < 2\sqrt{m} - 2\sqrt{m-1},$$

$$2\sqrt{m+2} - 2\sqrt{m+1} < \frac{1}{\sqrt{m+1}} < 2\sqrt{m+1} - 2\sqrt{m},$$

$$2\sqrt{m+3} - 2\sqrt{m+2} < \frac{1}{\sqrt{m+2}} < 2\sqrt{m+2} - 2\sqrt{m+1},$$

$$\cdots\cdots\cdots\cdots\cdots\cdots\cdots\cdots\cdots\cdots$$

$$2\sqrt{n+1} - 2\sqrt{n} < \frac{1}{\sqrt{n}} < 2\sqrt{n} - 2\sqrt{n-1}.$$

Adding these inequalities, we get

$$2\sqrt{n+1} - 2\sqrt{m} < \frac{1}{\sqrt{m}} + \frac{1}{\sqrt{m+1}} + \frac{1}{\sqrt{m+2}} + \cdots + \frac{1}{\sqrt{n}} <$$
$$< 2\sqrt{n} - 2\sqrt{m-1},$$

2. In the inequalities of Problem 1, suppose $m = 10{,}000$, $n = 1{,}000{,}000$, we then get

$$2\sqrt{1{,}000{,}001} - 2\sqrt{10{,}000} < \frac{1}{\sqrt{10{,}000}} +$$

$$+ \frac{1}{\sqrt{10{,}001}} + \cdots + \frac{1}{\sqrt{1{,}000{,}000}} < 2\sqrt{1{,}000{,}000} - 2\sqrt{9999}.$$

Since

$$2\sqrt{1{,}000{,}001} > 2\sqrt{1{,}000{,}000} = 2000, \quad 2\sqrt{10{,}000} = 200,$$
$$2\sqrt{9999} = \sqrt{39{,}996} > 199.98$$

(the latter inequality can be easily verified by extracting the square root to the nearest 0.01), then

$$2000 - 200 = 1800 < \frac{1}{\sqrt{10{,}000}} + \frac{1}{\sqrt{10{,}001}} + \cdots + \frac{1}{\sqrt{1{,}000{,}000}} <$$
$$< 2000 - 199.98 = 1800.02.$$

3. Multiplying the inequalities in Problem 2 by 50 we obtain in our notation

$$90{,}000 < 50z < 90{,}001,$$

hence

$$[50z] = 90{,}000.$$

4. For $n = 1$ the truth of the inequality

$$\frac{1}{2} \leqslant \frac{1}{\sqrt{3 \cdot 1 + 1}} = \frac{1}{2} \ ,$$

is obvious. Now, supposing that the inequality is true for $n = k$ that is

$$\frac{1}{2} \cdot \frac{3}{4} \cdot \frac{5}{6} \cdots \frac{2k-1}{2k} \leqslant \frac{1}{\sqrt{3k+1}} \ , \qquad (a)$$

we shall prove its truth for $n = k+1$, i.e. we shall prove that

$$\frac{1}{2} \cdot \frac{3}{4} \cdot \frac{5}{6} \cdots \frac{2k-1}{2k} \cdot \frac{2k+1}{2k+2} \leqslant \frac{1}{\sqrt{3k+4}} . \qquad (b)$$

Multiplying the inequality (a) by $\frac{2k+1}{2k+2}$ we obtain

$$\frac{1}{2} \cdot \frac{3}{4} \cdot \frac{5}{6} \cdots \frac{2k-1}{2k} \cdot \frac{2k+1}{2k+2} \leqslant \frac{1}{\sqrt{3k+1}} \cdot \frac{2k+1}{2k+2} .$$

It remains to prove the inequality

$$\frac{1}{\sqrt{3k+1}} \cdot \frac{2k+1}{2k+2} < \frac{1}{\sqrt{3k+4}} .$$

Multiplying it by $(2k+2) \sqrt{3k+1} \sqrt{3k+4}$ and squaring both sides of the resulting inequality we obtain

$$(2k+1)^2 (3k+4) < (2k+2)^2 (3k+1),$$

that is

$$12k^3 + 28k^2 + 19k + 4 < 12k^3 + 28k^2 + 20k + 4.$$

The last inequality is obvious as $k \geqslant 1$.   Thus it is proved that the inequality

$$\frac{1}{2} \cdot \frac{3}{4} \ldots \frac{2n-1}{2n} \leqslant \frac{1}{\sqrt{3n+1}}$$

is true for all n.

5. Putting $n = 50$ in the inequality of Problem 4 we get

$$\frac{1}{2} \cdot \frac{3}{4} \ldots \frac{99}{100} < \frac{1}{\sqrt{3 \cdot 50 + 1}} = \frac{1}{\sqrt{151}} < \frac{1}{\sqrt{144}} = \frac{1}{12}.$$

6. Putting $y = 6 - x$, $x = 6 - y$ we reduce the problem to finding the greatest value of the function

$$(6 - y) y^2 = 6y^2 - y^3$$

when $0 < y < 6$ Then, letting $y^2 = z$ we obtain the function

$$6z - z^{\frac{3}{2}},$$

whose greatest value (see note at the end of Problem 1, Section 4) is equal to

$$\left(\frac{3}{2} - 1\right)\left(\frac{6}{\frac{3}{2}}\right)^{\frac{\frac{3}{2}}{\frac{3}{2} - 1}} = 0.5 \cdot 4^3 = 32$$

and is reached at the point

$$z = \left(\frac{6}{\frac{3}{2}}\right)^{\frac{1}{\frac{3}{2} - 1}} = 4^2.$$

The function $6y^2 - y^3$ achieves its greatest value at the point $y = \sqrt{z} = 4$ and this value equals 32.

The function $x(6 - x)^2$ achieves its greatest value, 32, at the point $x = 6 - y = 6 - 4 = 2$.

7. The volume of the box (see Fig. 4 on page 34) is equal to

$$V = x(2a - 2x)^2 = 4x(a - x)^2, \quad 0 < x < a.$$

Putting $y = a - x$, $y^2 = z$, we get

$$V = 4\left(az - z^{\frac{3}{2}}\right).$$

The greatest value of the function $az - z^{\frac{3}{2}}$ is reached at the point

$$z = \left(\frac{a}{\frac{3}{2}}\right)^{\frac{1}{\frac{3}{2}-1}} = \left(\frac{2a}{3}\right)^{2}.$$

Consequently,

$$y = \sqrt{z} = \frac{2a}{3}, \quad x = a - y = a - \frac{2a}{3} = \frac{a}{3}.$$

Thus, the volume of the box is greatest when the length of the side of each cut-out square is a sixth of the length of the side of the given square.

8. The smallest value of the function $x^6 + 8x^2 + 5$ equals 5 and is reached when $x = 0$.

9. Putting $y = x^2$ we reduce the problem to finding the smallest value of the function

$$y^3 - 8y + 5$$

for positive values of y.

In Problem 1, Section 4, we proved that the smallest value of $y^3 - 8y$ equals

$$(1-3)\left(\frac{8}{3}\right)^{\frac{3}{3-1}} = -2\frac{8^{\frac{3}{2}}}{3^{\frac{3}{2}}} = -\frac{32\sqrt{6}}{9}.$$

The smallest value of the function $y^3 - 8y + 5$ equals

$$-\frac{32\sqrt{6}}{9} + 5 = -3.6\ldots$$

10. Putting $y = x^{\alpha}$ we obtain the function

$$y - ay^{\frac{1}{\alpha}} = a\left(\frac{1}{a}y - y^{\frac{1}{\alpha}}\right), \quad a > 0, \quad \frac{1}{\alpha} > 1.$$

By Problem 1, Section 4, the greatest value of the function $\frac{1}{a}y - y^{\frac{1}{a}}$ equals

$$\left(\frac{1}{a}-1\right)\left(\frac{\frac{1}{a}}{\frac{1}{a}}\right)^{\frac{\frac{1}{a}}{\frac{1}{a}-1}} = \left(\frac{1}{a}-1\right)\left(\frac{a}{a}\right)^{\frac{1}{1-a}} = \frac{1-a}{a}\left(\frac{a}{a}\right)^{\frac{1}{a-1}}.$$

Multiplying the last quantity by a, we find the greatest value of the function $a\left(\frac{1}{a}y - y^{\frac{1}{a}}\right)$ which, consequently, is equal to

$$(1-a)\frac{a}{a}\cdot\left(\frac{a}{a}\right)^{\frac{1}{a-1}} = (1-a)\left(\frac{a}{a}\right)^{1+\frac{1}{a-1}} = (1-a)\left(\frac{a}{a}\right)^{\frac{a}{a-1}}.$$

11. The function $\sqrt[4]{x} - 2x$, $x \geqslant 0$, $a = \frac{1}{4}$, $a = 2$, has its greatest value equal to

$$\left(1-\frac{1}{4}\right)\left(\frac{2}{\frac{1}{4}}\right)^{\frac{\frac{1}{4}}{\frac{1}{4}-1}} = \frac{3}{4}\cdot 8^{-\frac{1}{8}} = \frac{3}{8}.$$

It follows that for all $x \geqslant 0$ the following inequality holds:

$$\sqrt[4]{x} - 2x \leqslant \frac{3}{8}, \quad \text{or} \quad \sqrt[4]{x} \leqslant \frac{3}{8} + 2x.$$

12. Write down the inequality (7) of Section 2 in the form

$$\left(\frac{n+1}{n}\right)^n < e, \quad (n+1)^n < en^n.$$

If $n \geqslant 3 > e$ then

$$(n+1)^n < en^n < 3n^n \leqslant nn^n = n^{n+1}.$$

Raising both sides of the last inequality to the power $\frac{1}{n(n+1)}$ we obtain

$$\sqrt[n+1]{n+1} < \sqrt[n]{n}.$$

13. Since $1 < \sqrt{2} = \sqrt[6]{8} < \sqrt[6]{9} = \sqrt[3]{3}$, it follows that $\sqrt[3]{3}$ is the greatest of the numbers 1, $\sqrt{2}$, $\sqrt[3]{3}$. On the other hand, in the

previous problem we showed that the numbers $\sqrt[3]{3},\ \sqrt[4]{4},\ \ldots,\ \sqrt[n]{n},\ \ldots$
decrease, subsequently $\sqrt[3]{3}$ is the greatest of the numbers
$1,\ \sqrt{2},\ \sqrt[3]{3},\ \ldots,\ \sqrt[n]{n},\ \ldots$

14. Put $\sqrt[n]{n} = 1 + a_n,\ a_n > 0$. Raising to the power n, we get

$$n = (1 + a_n)^n = [(1 + a_n)^{\frac{n}{2}}]^2.$$

Supposing that $n \geqslant 2,\ \dfrac{n}{2} \geqslant 1$, then by Theorem 3, we get

$$(1 + a_n)^{\frac{n}{2}} > 1 + \frac{n}{2} a_n,\quad n > \left(1 + \frac{n}{2} a_n\right)^2 = 1 + n a_n + \frac{n^2}{4} a_n^2.$$

Hence it follows that

$$n > \frac{n^2}{4} a_n^2,\quad a_n^2 < \frac{4}{n},\quad a_n < \frac{2}{\sqrt{n}},\quad \sqrt[n]{n} = 1 + a_n < 1 + \frac{2}{\sqrt{n}}.$$

N o t e. Using Newton's binomial theorem it is easy to
verify that

$$\sqrt[n]{n} < 1 + \sqrt{\frac{2}{n}}.$$

Indeed

$$\left(1 + \sqrt{\frac{2}{n}}\right)^n = 1 + n\sqrt{\frac{2}{n}} + \frac{n(n-1)}{2}\frac{2}{n} + \ldots >$$
$$> 1 + \frac{n(n-1)}{2}\frac{2}{n} = n.$$

Hence it follows that

$$\sqrt[n]{n} < 1 + \sqrt{\frac{2}{n}}.$$

15. For $n = 1$ and $a_i > -1$ the inequality

$$1 + a_1 \geqslant 1 + a_1$$

is obvious. Suppose the inequality is true for $n = k$, i.e.

$$(1 + a_1)(1 + a_2) \ldots (1 + a_k) \geqslant 1 + a_1 + a_2 + \ldots + a_k.$$

Multiplying both sides of the inequality by $(1 + a_{k+1})$ we get:

$$(1 + a_1)(1 + a_2) \ldots (1 + a_k)(1 + a_{k+1}) \geqslant$$
$$\geqslant (1 + a_1 + a_2 + \ldots + a_k)(1 + a_{k+1}) =$$
$$= 1 + a_1 + \ldots + a_k + a_{k+1} + a_1 a_{k+1} + a_2 a_{k+1} + \ldots + a_k a_{k+1}.$$

Since the numbers $a_1, a_2, \ldots, a_k, a_{k+1}$ are of the same sign,

$$a_1 a_{k+1} + a_2 a_{k+1} + \ldots + a_k a_{k+1} \geqslant 0 \, ,$$

and consequently

$$(1 + a_1)(1 + a_2) \ldots (1 + a_k)(1 + a_{k+1}) \geqslant 1 + a_1 + a_2 + \ldots + a_k + a_{k+1},$$

i.e. the inequality is proved also for $n = k + 1$. This completes the proof of the truth of the inequality

$$(1 + a_1)(1 + a_2) \ldots (1 + a_n) \geqslant 1 + a_1 + a_2 + \ldots + a_n$$

for all n.

16. If the polynomial $(a_1 x - b_1)^2 + (a_2 x - b_2)^2 + \ldots + (a_n x - b_n)^2$ has a real root $x = x_1$, i.e.

$$(a_1 x_1 - b_1)^2 + (a_2 x_1 - b_2)^2 + \ldots + (a_n x_1 - b_n)^2 = 0,$$

then each of the numbers $a_1 x_1 - b_1, a_2 x_1 - b_2, \ldots, a_n x_1 - b_n$ equals zero, i.e.

$$0 = a_1 x_1 - b_1 = a_2 x_1 - b_2 = \ldots = a_n x_1 - b_n,$$
$$x_1 = \frac{b_1}{a_1} = \frac{b_2}{a_2} = \ldots = \frac{b_n}{a_n}.$$

Thus, we have proved that the polynomial

$$(a_1 x - b_1)^2 + (a_2 x - b_2)^2 + \ldots + (a_n x - b_n)^2 =$$
$$= x^2 (a_1^2 + a_2^2 + \ldots + a_n^2) - 2x (a_1 b_1 + a_2 b_2 + \ldots + a_n b_n) +$$
$$+ (b_1^2 + b_2^2 + \ldots + b_n^2)$$

cannot have two different real roots and, consequently

$$(a_1 b_1 + a_2 b_2 + \ldots + a_n b_n)^2 - (a_1^2 + \ldots + a_n^2)(b_1^2 + \ldots + b_n^2) \leqslant 0.$$

Hence we have the inequality (19)

$$(a_1 b_1 + a_2 b_2 + \ldots + a_n b_n)^2 \leqslant (a_1^2 + a_2^2 + \ldots + a_n^2)(b_1^2 + b_2^2 + \ldots + b_n^2).$$

Note that the sign of equality occurs only when the polynomial under discussion has a real root, i.e. when

$$\frac{a_1}{b_1} = \frac{a_2}{b_2} = \ldots = \frac{a_n}{b_n}.$$

17. Making use of the inequality (19) we obtain

$$c_1^2 = \left(\frac{a_1 + a_2 + \ldots + a_n}{n}\right)^2 = \left(\frac{a_1}{\sqrt{n}} \frac{1}{\sqrt{n}} + \ldots + \frac{a_n}{\sqrt{n}} \frac{1}{\sqrt{n}}\right)^2 \leqslant$$

$$\leqslant \left(\frac{a_1^2}{n} + \frac{a_2^2}{n} + \ldots + \frac{a_n^2}{n}\right) \underbrace{\left(\frac{1}{n} + \frac{1}{n} + \ldots + \frac{1}{n}\right)}_{n} =$$

$$= \frac{a_1^2 + a_2^2 + \ldots + a_n^2}{n} = c_2^2.$$

It then follows that

$$c_1 \leqslant c_2$$

(the arithmetic mean does not exceed the quadratic mean).

18. From the inequality

$$(\sqrt{n+1} + \sqrt{n-1})^2 = n + 1 + 2\sqrt{n^2-1} + n - 1 =$$
$$= 2n + 2\sqrt{n^2-1} < 2n + 2\sqrt{n^2} = 4n,$$

it follows that

$$\sqrt{n+1} + \sqrt{n-1} < 2\sqrt{n},$$

$$\frac{1}{2\sqrt{n}} < \frac{1}{\sqrt{n+1} + \sqrt{n-1}} =$$

$$= \frac{\sqrt{n+1} - \sqrt{n-1}}{(\sqrt{n+1} + \sqrt{n-1})(\sqrt{n+1} - \sqrt{n-1})} = \frac{\sqrt{n+1} - \sqrt{n-1}}{2}.$$

Multiplying by 2, we obtain

$$\frac{1}{\sqrt{n}} < \sqrt{n+1} - \sqrt{n-1}.$$

19. In the inequality of Exercise 18 we put $n = 2, 3, \ldots, n$:

$$\frac{1}{\sqrt{2}} < \sqrt{3} - 1,$$

$$\frac{1}{\sqrt{3}} < \sqrt{4} - \sqrt{2},$$

$$\frac{1}{\sqrt{4}} < \sqrt{5} - \sqrt{3},$$

$$\frac{1}{\sqrt{5}} < \sqrt{6} - \sqrt{4},$$

$$\cdots \cdots \cdots$$

$$\frac{1}{\sqrt{n}} < \sqrt{n+1} - \sqrt{n-1}.$$

Adding these inequalities we get

$$\frac{1}{\sqrt{2}} + \frac{1}{\sqrt{3}} + \ldots + \frac{1}{\sqrt{n}} < \sqrt{n+1} + \sqrt{n} - \sqrt{2} - 1.$$

Finally, adding 1 to both sides of the inequality, we obtain

$$1 + \frac{1}{\sqrt{2}} + \frac{1}{\sqrt{3}} + \frac{1}{\sqrt{4}} + \frac{1}{\sqrt{5}} + \ldots + \frac{1}{\sqrt{n}} < \sqrt{n+1} + \sqrt{n} - \sqrt{2}.$$

N o t e.   In Section 1 it was proved that

$$1 + \frac{1}{\sqrt{2}} + \frac{1}{\sqrt{3}} + \ldots + \frac{1}{\sqrt{n}} > 2\sqrt{n+1} - 2\sqrt{2} + 1.$$

The numbers $\sqrt{n+1} + \sqrt{n} - \sqrt{2}$ and $2\sqrt{n+1} - 2\sqrt{2} + 1$ differ from each other by less than 0.42. Each of these numbers can be taken for the approximate value of the sum

$$1 + \frac{1}{\sqrt{2}} + \frac{1}{\sqrt{3}} + \ldots + \frac{1}{\sqrt{n}} = z_n.$$

Note, without proof, that the number $\sqrt{n+1} + \sqrt{n} - \sqrt{2}$ differs less from the number z_n than does the number $2\sqrt{n+1} - 2\sqrt{2} + 1$.

20. The function $\frac{x^3}{x^4 + 5}$ takes negative values when $x < 0$.

It follows that the greatest value of the function is reached when x is positive.

Since

$$\frac{x^3}{x^4+5} = \frac{1}{5\left(\frac{1}{5}x + x^{-3}\right)},$$

the greatest value of the function is achieved at that point where the function $\frac{1}{5}x + x^{-3}$ takes its smallest value. From the Problem 5 of Section 4 it follows that the smallest value of this function equals

$$(1+3)\left(\frac{\frac{1}{5}}{3}\right)^{\frac{-3}{-3-1}} = 4\left(\frac{1}{15}\right)^{\frac{3}{4}}.$$

The greatest value of the function $\frac{x^3}{x^4+5}$ equals

$$\frac{1}{5 \cdot 4 \cdot \left(\frac{1}{15}\right)^{\frac{3}{4}}} = \frac{15^{\frac{3}{4}}}{20} = \frac{15}{20\sqrt[4]{15}} = \frac{3}{4\sqrt[4]{15}}.$$

To find the greatest value of the function $x^6 - 0.6x^{10}$, put $y = x^6$. It is clear that $y \geqslant 0$. The function

$$y - 0.6y^{\frac{10}{6}} = 0.6\left(\frac{10}{6}y - y^{\frac{10}{6}}\right)$$

takes the greatest value (see Problem 1, Section 4)

$$0.6\left(\frac{10}{6}-1\right)\left(\frac{\frac{10}{6}}{\frac{10}{6}}\right)^{\frac{\frac{10}{6}}{\frac{10}{6}-1}} = 0.4.$$

21. In this problem, let $y = \frac{1}{x^2}$. We get

$$\sqrt{x} + \frac{a}{x^2} = y^{-\frac{1}{4}} + ay.$$

The smallest value of the function $y^{-\frac{1}{4}} + ay$ (Problem 5, Section 4) equals

$$\left(1 + \frac{1}{4}\right)(4a)^{\frac{1}{5}} = \frac{5}{4}(4a)^{\frac{1}{5}}.$$

Putting $\frac{5}{4}(4a)^{\frac{1}{5}} = 2.5$, we get

$$(4a)^{\frac{1}{5}} = 2, \quad 4a = 32, \quad a = 8.$$

22. $S = 1 - \frac{1}{2^2} + \frac{1}{3^2} - \frac{1}{4^2} + \frac{1}{5^2} - \frac{1}{6^2} + \ldots =$

$$= \left(1 + \frac{1}{2^2} + \frac{1}{3^2} + \frac{1}{4^2} + \frac{1}{5^2} + \frac{1}{6^2} + \ldots\right) - 2\left(\frac{1}{2^2} + \frac{1}{4^2} + \frac{1}{6^2} + \ldots\right) =$$

$$= \left(1 + \frac{1}{2^2} + \frac{1}{3^2} + \frac{1}{4^2} + \frac{1}{5^2} + \frac{1}{6^2} + \ldots\right) - \frac{2}{2^2}\left(1 + \frac{1}{2^2} + \frac{1}{3^2} + \ldots\right) =$$

$$= \frac{1}{2}\left(1 + \frac{1}{2^2} + \frac{1}{3^2} + \ldots\right) = \frac{1}{2}\frac{\pi^2}{6} = \frac{\pi^2}{12}$$

(We used the equation (27).)

23.   Since $a > 0$ then $a + 1 > 1$ and, consequently,

$$\left(1 + \frac{1}{n}\right)^{1+a} > 1 + \frac{1+a}{n},$$

$$\left(1 - \frac{1}{n}\right)^{1+a} > 1 - \frac{1+a}{n}.$$

Multiplying these inequalities by n^{1+a} we get:

$$(n+1)^{1+a} > n^{1+a} + (1+a)n^a,$$
$$(n-1)^{1+a} > n^{1+a} - (1+a)n^a.$$

It follows from these inequalities that

$$\frac{n^{1+a} - (n-1)^{1+a}}{1+a} < n^a < \frac{(n+1)^{1+a} - n^{1+a}}{1+a}.$$

Writing out these inequalities for values of $n = 1, 2, 3, \ldots, n$:

$$\frac{1}{1+a} < 1 < \frac{2^{1+a} - 1}{1+a},$$

$$\frac{2^{1+a} - 1}{1+a} < 2^a < \frac{3^{1+a} - 2^{1+a}}{1+a},$$

$$\cdots\cdots\cdots\cdots\cdots\cdots$$

$$\frac{n^{1+a} - (n-1)^{1+a}}{1+a} < n^a < \frac{(n+1)^{1+a} - n^{1+a}}{1+a},$$

and adding we get

$$\frac{n^{1+a}}{1+a} < 1 + 2^a + 3^a + \ldots + n^a < \frac{(n+1)^{1+a} - 1}{1+a} < \frac{(n+1)^{1+a}}{1+a}.$$

24. From the inequalities in Exercise 23 it follows that

$$\frac{1}{1+a} < \frac{1 + 2^a + 3^a + \ldots + n^a}{n^{1+a}} < \frac{\left(1 + \frac{1}{n}\right)^{1+a}}{1+a}.$$

The left-hand side of the last inequality is the constant number $\frac{1}{1+a}$, and the right-hand side tends to a limit (equal to $\frac{1}{1+a}$) when n tends to infinity. Consequently, the middle part of the inequalities also tends to the same limit, i.e.

$$\lim_{n \to \infty} \frac{1 + 2^a + 3^a + \ldots + n^a}{n^{1+a}} = \frac{1}{1+a}.$$

25. Let us introduce the following notation:

$$A^3 = a_1^3 + a_2^3 + \ldots + a_n^3, \quad B^3 = b_1^3 + b_2^3 + \ldots + b_n^3,$$
$$C^3 = c_1^3 + c_2^3 + \ldots + c_n^3,$$
$$x_1 = \frac{a_1}{A}, \ x_2 = \frac{a_2}{A}, \ \ldots, \ x_n = \frac{a_n}{A}, \ y_1 = \frac{b_1}{B}, \ y_2 = \frac{b_2}{B}, \ldots, \ y_n = \frac{b_n}{B},$$
$$z_1 = \frac{c_1}{C}, \ z_2 = \frac{c_2}{C}, \ \ldots, \ z_n = \frac{c_n}{C}.$$

From the inequalities (10), we have

$$a_1 b_1 c_1 = ABC x_1 y_1 z_1 \leqslant ABC \frac{x_1^3 + y_1^3 + z_1^3}{3},$$
$$a_2 b_2 c_2 = ABC x_2 y_2 z_2 \leqslant ABC \frac{x_2^3 + y_2^3 + z_2^3}{3},$$
$$\cdot \ \cdot \ \cdot \ \cdot \ \cdot \ \cdot \ \cdot \ \cdot \ \cdot \ \cdot \ \cdot \ \cdot \ \cdot \ \cdot$$
$$a_n b_n c_n = ABC x_n y_n z_n \leqslant ABC \frac{x_n^3 + y_n^3 + z_n^3}{3}.$$

Adding these inequalities we obtain

$$(a_1 b_1 c_1 + a_2 b_2 c_2 + \ldots + a_n b_n c_n) \leqslant$$
$$\leqslant ABC \left(\frac{x_1^3 + x_2^3 + \ldots + x_n^3}{3} + \frac{y_1^3 + y_2^3 + \ldots + y_n^3}{3} + \frac{z_1^3 + z_2^3 + \ldots + z_n^3}{3} \right).$$

Taking into account the notation which we have introduced, it is easy to calculate that

$$x_1^3 + x_2^3 + \ldots + x_n^3 = \frac{a_1^3 + a_2^3 + \ldots + a_n^3}{A^3} = \frac{A^3}{A^3} = 1,$$
$$y_1^3 + y_2^3 + \ldots + y_n^3 = 1, \quad z_1^3 + z_2^3 + \ldots + z_n^3 = 1.$$

Consequently

$$(a_1b_1c_1 + a_2b_2c_2 + \ldots + a_nb_nc_n) \leqslant ABC\left(\frac{1}{3} + \frac{1}{3} + \frac{1}{3}\right) = ABC.$$

Cubing both sides of the inequality, we finally get

$$(a_1b_1c_1 + a_2b_2c_2 + \ldots + a_nb_nc_n)^3 \leqslant A^3B^3C^3 =$$
$$= (a_1^3 + a_2^3 + \ldots + a_n^3)(b_1^3 + b_2^3 + \ldots + b_n^3)(c_1^3 + c_2^3 + \ldots + c_n^3).$$

26. Let us write down the inequalities (24) for various values of n:

$$\ln\frac{n+1}{n} < \frac{1}{n} < \ln\frac{n}{n-1},$$
$$\ln\frac{n+2}{n+1} < \frac{1}{n+1} < \ln\frac{n+1}{n},$$
$$\cdots\cdots\cdots\cdots\cdots\cdots$$
$$\ln\frac{kn+1}{kn} < \frac{1}{kn} < \ln\frac{kn}{kn-1}.$$

Adding these inequalities we get

$$\ln\frac{(n+1)(n+2)\ldots(kn+1)}{n(n+1)\ldots kn} < \frac{1}{n} + \frac{1}{n+1} + \ldots + \frac{1}{kn} <$$
$$< \ln\left[\frac{n}{n-1}\cdot\frac{n+1}{n}\ldots\frac{kn}{kn-1}\right],$$

i.e.

$$\ln\frac{kn+1}{n} = \ln\left(k + \frac{1}{n}\right) <$$
$$< \frac{1}{n} + \frac{1}{n+1} + \frac{1}{n+2} + \ldots + \frac{1}{kn} < \ln\frac{kn}{n-1} = \ln\left(k + \frac{k}{n-1}\right).$$

If n tends to infinity, then $\ln\left(k + \frac{1}{n}\right)$ tends to $\ln k$ and $\ln\left(k + \frac{k}{n-1}\right)$ tends to the same limit. Consequently.

$$\lim_{n\to\infty}\left(\frac{1}{n} + \frac{1}{n+1} + \ldots + \frac{1}{kn}\right) = \ln k.$$